Songs of Hope and Peace

Songs of Hope and Peace

Illinois Chapter
United Church of Christ Fellowship
in the Arts

The Pilgrim Press
New York

Library of Congress Cataloging-in-Publication Data

Songs of hope and peace.

Hymns, songs, service music, and anthems.

1. Hymns, English.   2. Anthems.   3. Hope—Songs and music.   4. Peace—Songs and music.   I. Chávez-Melo, Skinner.   II. United Church of Christ. Fellowship in the Arts. Illinois Chapter.

M2131.U62S6 1987   87-751745
                    ISBN 0-8298-0710-1 (pbk.)

The Pilgrim Press, 132 West 31 Street, New York, NY 10001

Contents

Introduction

The Illinois Chapter of the United Church of Christ Fellowship in the Arts is pleased to present this gift of word and music to the whole church. *Songs of Hope and Peace* celebrates both the thirtieth anniversary of the United Church of Christ, and the designation of the church's priority as a "just peace" church.

Established in 1957 as a merger of the former Congregational-Christian Churches and the Evangelical and Reformed Church, the United Church of Christ continues to be a uniting Christian community expressing the faith in many ways through a unifying spirit. This book reflects that unity within diversity. The United Church of Christ continues its high commitment to peace and justice in our world.

Invitations for creative contributions to this project were sent to all the conferences of the United Church of Christ. Entries were received from 25 conferences, including over 250 works primarily from local church members. Contributors to this hope and peace resource represent persons of all ages, clergy and laity, from urban and rural communities.

The Illinois Chapter of the United Church of Christ Fellowship in the Arts (UCCFA) envisioned this resource in 1983, noting an outpouring of songs in this challenging time with few opportunities to publish them. By 1984, after a mailing to all of the conferences and an article in the Christmas 1983 issue of UCCFA's *Arts Advocate*, entries began arriving to be reviewed by an Illinois jury. Mr. Sam Hill, minister of music at St. Paul's United Church of Christ, Chicago, Illinois, and Mr. Michael Surratt, minister of music at Union Church, Hinsdale, Illinois, selected the works to be submitted for publication consideration. The final editing was completed by Mr. Skinner Chávez-Melo, who clarified and corrected the music manuscripts as music editor for *Songs of Hope and Peace*. Mr. Chávez-Melo also serves as music editor *Albricias*, a Spanish hymnal of The Episcopal Church. He was commissioned by the United Church Board for Homeland Ministries (UCBHM) to complete the task begun by the Illinois Chapter of UCCFA under the guidance of its co-chairperson, Laini Zinn. Encouraged by the Council of the Illinois Conference of the United Church of Christ, the Illinois Chapter of UCCFA received a grant for this songbook from the UCBHM through its Executive Vice President, Dr. C. Shelby Rooks.

Our gratitude is also extended to the Division of Education and Publication of the UCBHM for a job well done, and for helping to complete our dream. Special thanks to Dr. Larry E. Kalp, Secretary for Publications, Ms. Marion Meyer, Senior Book Editor of The Pilgrim Press, and Mr. Jack H. Haney, Editor of Curriculum Services. Mr. Haney attended to the copyright legalities and permissions as well as served as editorial supervisor of the publication. Without Mr. Chávez-Melo's work, the final publication could not have done justice to these collected gifts of word and music freely offered by their creators. Any royalties realized from this publication will be used by the Illinois Chapter UCCFA to support future program resources and projects.

Though the majority of the songs published in *Songs of Hope and Peace* are new in both word and tune, you will also discover fresh words put to some familiar or forgotten hymn tunes. Recognizing the hesitancy of some congregations to try new material, the jury had as a selection priority "the singable quality" of each work. Perhaps youth and adult choirs will develop ways for sharing this rich resource by having a "hymn of the month" in their congregation's worship.

No single collection of music can completely reflect the talents, dedication and diversity of musicians and poets of our church in this time. I can only join in the celebration of the Christian faith through hope and peace. We recognize that these original creative expressions will serve as supplements to existing hymnody, and enlarge on the themes of unity, justice, and peace. Due to the limitations of space and production costs, this is only a sampling of the excellent work offered by nationally known musicians within our church family. Their songs and recordings have brought a fresh spirit to our youth events, women's gatherings, regional meetings, and sessions of the General Synod. We are grateful and celebrate their creative ministries. Included among these musicians are Don Eaton of Oregon, Glenn Wallace of New York, Martie Swan of Ohio, Susan Saville of Maine, Dosia Carlson of Arizona, Gary Miller of Illinois, Ruth Duck of Massachusetts, Ron Klussmeier of Wisconsin, and Jane Parker Huber of Indiana.

Finally, for the patience and work of nurturing this project from its birth to its publication, thanks to the members of the Illinois Chapter of UCCFA and its co-chair, Ms. Georgene Corbitt.

LAINI ZINN

A Ship That Calls Itself the Church

Martin G. Schneider
Tr. Mary N. Hawkes, 1983

Martin G. Schneider

Boldly (♩ = 96), *in unison*

1. A___ ship that calls it-self the Church,___ The voyage of time its
2. That___ ship that calls it-self the Church,___ Oft lies in har-bor
3. In the ship that calls it-self the Church,___ Each du-ty's glad-ly

sea, Knows where to go be-cause its aim___ Is God's e-ter-ni-
fast, Be-cause life is more com-fort-a-ble___ While look-ing to the
done, Or each one goes a dif-f'rent way___ And feels lost and a-

ty. The ship moves on with threats of storm Through dan-ger, risk, and
past. But if we risk and dan-ger fear, We lose our sight of
lone. When each one glad-ly does a job, And each works with the

fear, De-spair, hope, strug-gle, vic-to-ry; It
God, Who in the wise but qui-et voice, Will
whole, The fear and lone-li-ness dis-solve, As

trav - els year on year. And still a - gain one
be our strength and guide. On - ly if we take
each per - forms a role. And so we trav - el

asks one - self;__ Will it be-calmed re - main, Or
ven - tures on__ Will we our goal at - tain: To
far and wide__ On this trip through the sea, With

per - ish in the rest-less sea,__ Its goal not to at - tain?
live in peace and fu - ture hope__ With God's own love our aim.
friends we love and serve and act__ In true com - mu - ni - ty.

O stay by us,__ God; O__ stay by us,__ God; Or__

else we're a-lone on the trip through the sea, O stay by us, God.

Text and Mel.: Martin G. Schneider; Text engl.: Mary N. Hawkes; © Gustav Bosse Verlag Regensburg.

The young people of Heilandskirche in West Berlin loved this hymn, which brings us a message of the need for the ecumenical church. Mary Hawkes, translator of these words, worked with these young people in the late 1960s.

Believe, Be Alive and Free

Glenn Wallace

Irregular with Refrain
Glenn Wallace

Refrain

Be - lieve, be a - live and free,_____ have
faith in hu - man - i - ty; With u - ni -
ty we'll al - ways be - lieve be a - live and free.

1. Pro - vide for us each day,_____ pro -
2. With jus - tice as our goal _____ and
3. For fam - 'ly and our friends,_____ for

tect us on our way, For - give our
peace with - in our soul, We'll work to
all the gifts God sends In all your

sins and en - ter in, for all these things we pray.
feed every hu - man need and God can make us whole.
ways, we give you praise for love that nev - er ends.

3   Breathe on Me, Breath of God

Edwin Hatch, 1835–1889
Adapted by Laini Zinn

S.M.
Laini Zinn

love_____ what Thou dost love and do, what
Thee_____ I will one will, and to do what and
earth ly part of me glows with Thy

Dm7 · G · G#dim

Thou would do. Breathe on me, Breath of God,
to en - dure. Breathe on me, Breath of God,
fire di - vine. Breathe on me, Breath of God,

Am · F7 · Am7 · D9

1. 2. · **3.**

This I pray. This I pray.
This I pray.

G9 · C · G7 · D♭7 · Cmaj7

4   Called as Partners in Christ's Service

Jane Parker Huber

RUSTINGTON 87.87.D
C. Hubert H. Parry, 1848–1918

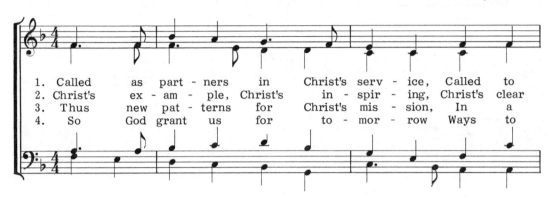

1. Called as part - ners in Christ's serv - ice, Called to
2. Christ's ex - am - ple, Christ's in - spir - ing, Christ's clear
3. Thus new pat - terns for Christ's mis - sion, In a
4. So God grant us for to - mor - row Ways to

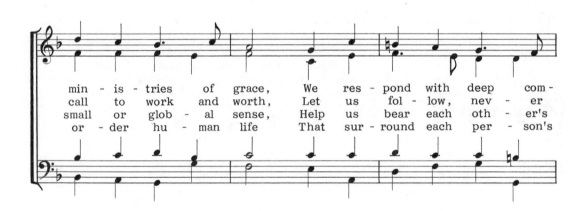

min - is - tries of grace, We res - pond with deep com -
call to work and worth, Let us fol - low, nev - er
small or glob - al sense, Help us bear each oth - er's
or - der hu - man life That sur - round each per - son's

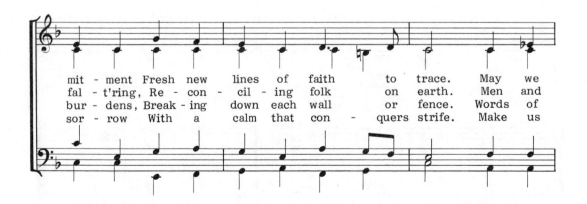

mit - ment Fresh new lines of faith to trace. May we
fal - t'ring, Re - con - cil - ing folk on earth. Men and
bur - dens, Break - ing down each wall or fence. Words of
sor - row With a calm that con - quers strife. Make us

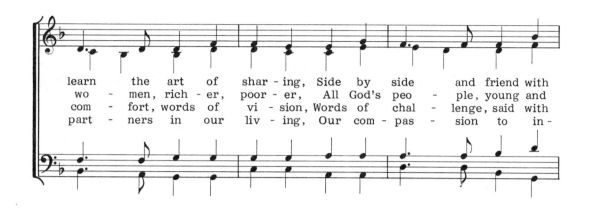

learn the art of shar - ing, Side by side and friend with
wo - men, rich - er, poor - er, All God's peo - ple, young and
com - fort, words of vi - sion, Words of chal - lenge, said with
part - ners in our liv - ing, Our com - pas - sion to in -

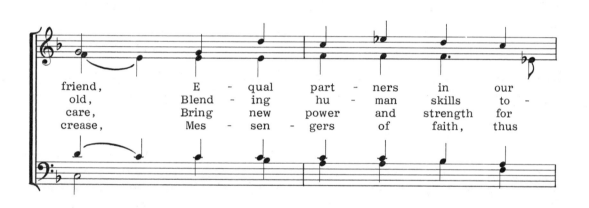

friend, E - qual part - ners in our
old, Blend - ing hu - man skills to -
care, Bring new power and strength for
crease, Mes - sen - gers of faith, thus

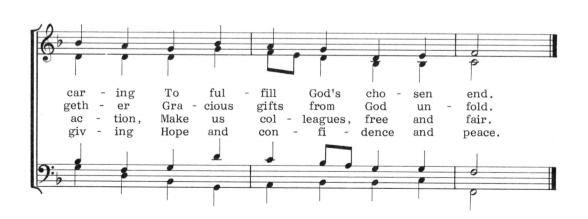

car - ing To ful - fill God's cho - sen end.
geth - er Gra - cious gifts from God un - fold.
ac - tion, Make us col - leagues, free and fair.
giv - ing Hope and con - fi - dence and peace.

5   Christ Has Come to Bring Us News

Isaiah 61; Luke 4:18
Adapted by Laini Zinn

Irregular
Laini Zinn

1. Christ has come to bring us news that God in - tends to
2. Lead us in the paths of good-ness. Give us strength to

set at lib - er - ty Those who are cap - tive, Those who are bro - ken,
meet new chal-leng-es. Share with each oth - er, Care for each oth - er,

All who are blind shall see. Mes - si - ah comes to be re -
Give and re-ceive in love. The way of life that Christ has

vealed, as hu - man needs are met and healed.
shown will be re - vealed as love is known.

Refrain *(with congregation)*

Make of us___ Thy SER - VANT PEO-PLE;___ Make of us Thy

HO-LY___ CHURCH.___ Fill us with Thy LOV - ING___SPIR-IT;___

1. | 2.

Help us bring Sha - lom___ on Earth.___ lom___ on Earth.___ 3. So

jour - ney in-to wil - der-ness to find___new ways to be more hu-man; to

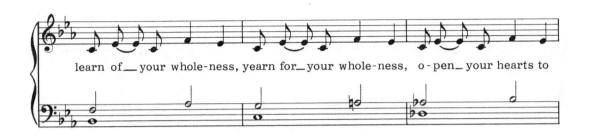

learn of—your whole-ness, yearn for—your whole-ness, o-pen— your hearts to

love. So that Sha - lom may make us— one——— with God our

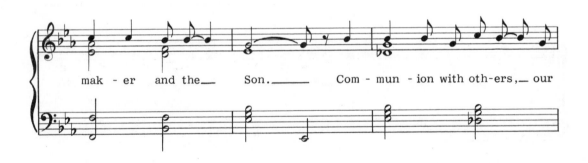

mak - er and the— Son.——— Com - mun - ion with oth-ers,— our

sis - ters and broth-ers,— Will bring God's reign of Peace on Earth.

Christ the Crucified

James W. Crawford

WESTMINSTER ABBEY 87.87.87
Henry Purcell, 1659–1695, adapt.

1. Christ the cru - ci - fied, God's Sav - ior, Christ tri - um - phant this
2. Christ the ris - en, Con - qu'ring Sav - ior, Set - ting hearts___ at
3. Christ as - cen - dant, Gra - cious Sav - ior, Sov - 'reign Ser - vant
4. Christ Re - deem - er, God Cre - a - tor, Spir't en - ab - ler, the

Eas - ter Day, Vic - tor o'er the bonds of e - vil,
lib - er - ty, Off - 'ring to the pris - 'ner free - dom,
pro - mised Peace, Faith's Foun - da - tion, Hope's Sure Fu - ture,
Three in One, Un - der - gird - ing earth and Heav - en,

From dark pow'rs___ do us___ con - vey Through the Tree you
Op - 'ning blind - ed eyes___ to see: Born in weak - ness,
Grant - ing cap - tive souls___ re - lease, Beck - 'ning all to
Re - con - cil - ing life___ as Son. Con - se - crate us,

wrought sal - va - tion, Showed the world how love o - beys.
serv - ing bold - ly, Bear - er of Love's vic - to - ry.
loy - al ser - vice, Chang - ing each to love's in - crease.
bless - ed Spir - it, 'til on earth Love's reign is won.

7 Come, Christians, Journey Forth

(Cristianos, Avanzad con Nuestro Creador)

Laini Zinn
Spanish trans., Raquel Achón

PURDUE Irregular
Laini Zinn

1. Come, Chris-tians, jour-ney forth with our Cre - a - tor, God, Re-
2. We own our Cov - e - nant, each in a spe - cial way, Af-

flect - ing "Sha - lom" on earth.___ Where out of cha - os
firm - ing through signs of faith.___ Each u - nique soul is

or - der___ is formed and each new be - ing finds a new
one with___ the Lord as we pro - claim God's name___ to-

worth._____ Be - hold God pre-sents a mys - ter - y, A
day._____ Our faith re - di-rects our en - er-gies to

love cast - ing out all fear. He en - ters in-to our his - to - ry, re -
flow with the high-est good. Our trust gives us a com - mu - ni - ty to

new - ing hope and cheer. Thy flam - ing tongues of fire fill us a -
grow in per - son - hood. Come, Chris-tians, live the faith, jour-ney a -

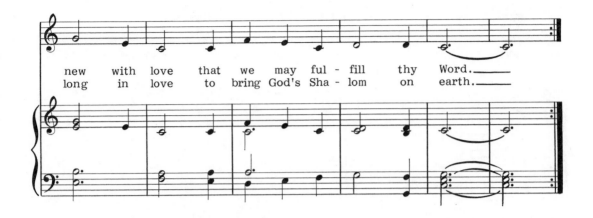

new with love that we may ful - fill thy Word.____
long in love to bring God's Sha - lom on earth.____

1. Cristianos, avanzad con nuestro Creador.
   Shalom sea por doquier.
   Y surge orden aún del caos,
   nuevo valor encuentra el ser.
   Y Dios nos revela un misterio
   amor venciendo el temor.
   Envió a su Hijo a la historia y
   aún con nos está.
   Su fuego ardiente invádenos con amor,
   al cumplir su voluntad.

2. Tenemos nuestro pacto siendo muy especial
   afirmando nuestra fe.
   Cada alma es única en el Señor
   y proclamamos su nombre hoy.
   La fe redirige la energía
   y fluye con fiel bondad
   Construímos una comunidad
   basada en dignidad.
   Vivamos esta fe, vivamos con amor
   y Dios nos dará Shalom.

Spanish translation by Raquel Achon

Come, Let Us Honor Those Who Led the Way 8

Harriet Ilse Ziegenhals

TOULON 10.10.10.10.
Abridged from Genevan Psalter, 1551

1. Come, let us hon - or those who led the way;
2. In years of tur - moil, bit - ter - ness and pain,
3. Praise now and thanks un - to our God we bring;

Wo - men of Scrip - ture wit - ness - ing each day;
Wo - men have sought e - qua - li - ty to gain,
Lift - ing each voice, with cour - age let us sing;

Teach - er and lead - er, queen and proph - et - ess,
No long - er dwell up - on the past with tears,
To - geth - er we'll not from our pur - pose swerve,

Through vi - tal min - is - try their faith con - fess.
Pledge new com - mit - ment for the fu - ture years.
Build - ing the whole - ness of the Church we serve.

9 Come, Peace Of God

May Rowland

PAX 10.10.10.10.
Lily Rundle

1. Come! Peace of God, and dwell again on earth,
2. Break ev - ery wea - pon forged in fires of hate,
3. Bring self - ish lives from shad - ow - lands of loss
4. Come! Bless - ed Peace, as when, in hush of eve,

Come, with the calm that hailed Thy Prin - ce's birth,
Turn back the foes that would as - sail Thy gate;
In - to the ra - diance of the Sav - iour's cross,
God's ben - e - dic - tion falls on souls who grieve;

Come, with the heal - ing of Thy gen - tle touch,
Where fields of strife lie des - o - late and bare
Where, in that gift— so pre - cious, yet so lone—
As shines a star when wea - ry day de - parts,

Come, Peace of God, that this world needs so much.
Take Thy sweet flow'rs of peace and plant them there.
Life finds its broth - er - hood and love its throne.
Come! Peace of God, and rule with - in our hearts.

From Dawn of Time

James W. Crawford

THE EIGHTH TUNE L.M.
Thomas Tallis, 1505?–1585

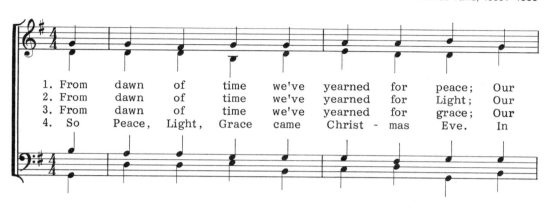

1. From dawn of time we've yearned for peace; Our
2. From dawn of time we've yearned for Light; Our
3. From dawn of time we've yearned for grace; Our
4. So Peace, Light, Grace came Christ - mas Eve. In

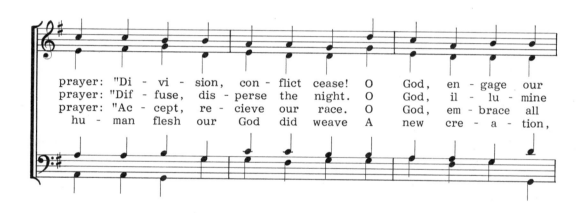

prayer: "Di - vi - sion, con - flict cease! O God, en - gage our
prayer: "Dif - fuse, dis - perse the night. O God, il - lu - mine
prayer: "Ac - cept, re - cieve our race. O God, em - brace all
hu - man flesh our God did weave A new cre - a - tion,

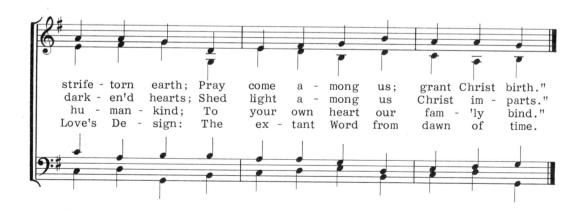

strife - torn earth; Pray come a - mong us; grant Christ birth."
dark - en'd hearts; Shed light a - mong us Christ im - parts."
hu - man - kind; To your own heart our fam - 'ly bind."
Love's De - sign: The ex - tant Word from dawn of time.

11 Go Tell It on the Mountain

Afro-American Spiritual
Adapt. Paul Gregory

GO TELL IT ON THE MOUNTAIN 76.76 with Refrain.
Afro-American Spiritual, 19th Cent.

Unison

Go, tell it on the moun - tain, O-ver the hills and ev -'ry-where;

Fine

Go, tell it on the moun - tain that Je - sus Christ_ is Lord.

Harmony

1. The poor now hear good ti - dings As jus - tice sets them free, And
2. The cap-tive's will is strength-ened As con-science makes its stand; The
3. Each lone - ly heart be-friend - ed, Brought peace and u - ni - ty; A
4. We'll be a church pro-claim - ing That faith and work are one; That

D.C.

find that Christ has pro - mised Life will a - bun-dant be._____
bonds of fear are loos - ened, Love lights earth's dark-ened lands._____
sick world finds its heal - ing In Love Christ's life sets free._____
life must be self - giv - ing And car - ing's ne - ver done._____

God Alone is Still Our God

Richard B. Kozelka

7.6.7.6.6.7.7.8.
David Cicchese

1. "God a-lone is still our God." Sing our spir-its wak - ing.
2. "God a-lone is still our God." Faith to faith_ de-clar - ing:
3. "God a-lone is still our God." Age to age_ ex-tend - ing.

Power of be - ing, still our God, Death and dark - ness_ break - ing.
Past and pres-ent, still our God, Hope and haz-ard with us shar - ing.
O'er the king-dom, still our God, Peace and pow-er com-pre-hend - ing.

So we raise songs of praise, to the God who grants our days:
So we sing, as we bring hearts to God, re - mem - ber - ing:
We ac-claim, God's great name, now and ev - er more the same:

Now and ev - er, still our God, Good things mak-ing and par-tak - ing.
In all sea-sons, still our God, Bless - ings bear-ing and pre-par - ing.
Down the fu-ture, still our God, Spir - it send-ing and in-tend - ing.

13

God is Our Strength

Laini Zinn

10.10.10.10.8.8.8.8.11.10.10.10.10
Laini Zinn

God is our strength, Our Fa - ther and Moth - er;

There is no oth - er who can bring Sha - lom.

When we're a - fraid, we'll trust in God's gui - dance,

When all else fright - ens, God will be our home.

Choir or Quartet

Let's beat our swords to plow - shares strong; Till - ing the

soil for seeds of peace. Re - new our hopes to

weed out wrong; Trans - form our fears so wars will

cease. May our prayers be as one, that God's will be___ done.

Congregation
a tempo

God is our strength, So let go of weap-ons; False hope and ha-tred

a tempo

nev-er come from Love. God needs our hearts, our hands and our

spir-its Work-ing to-geth-er 'til God's world is one.

rit.

God, of Our Life, of All That We Encounter 14

Mary N. Hawkes, 1966
Adapted, 1983

ISTE CONFESSOR (ROUEN) 11.11.11.5
Poitiers Antiphoner, 1746

Moderately (♩=116)

1. God of our life, of all that we en - coun - ter,
2. We know that of - ten we must learn through strug - gles,
3. In fam - 'ly liv - ing, day to day with neigh - bor,
4. For this, our Church, we pray with deep sin - cer - i - ty,

We thank you now for all you love and give to us;
Through strife and strain we grow and learn a - bout our - selves;
We need to know that you are al - ways with us;
That it may ev - er see new ways of min - is - try,

For food and home and all our dai - ly
We find it so hard to love our neigh - bor
In each re - la - tion - ship, we may see your
To those who live in ru - ral place or

sus - te - nance, Thank you, O God of Life.
as our - selves; Teach us, O God of Growth.
pres - ence; Guide us, O Nur - tur - er.
cit - y; Help us, O God of Love.

The words to this hymn are dedicated to Jessie N. and William E. Hawkes.

15 God Our Maker and Sustainer

Lillian Schwerdfager

RAQUEL 87.87.D.
Skinner Chávez-Melo

1. God our Ma - ker and Sus -
2. By our Sav - iour's grace and
3. Though your law is of - ten
4. Sins of doubt - ing, greed and

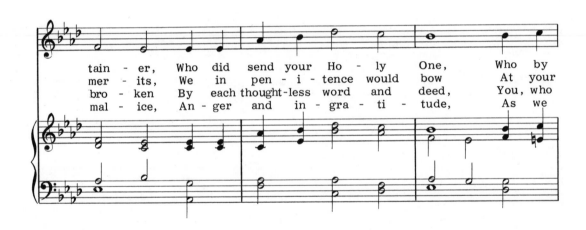

tain - er, Who did send your Ho - ly One, Who by
mer - its, We in pen - i - tence would bow At your
bro - ken By each thought-less word and deed, You, who
mal - ice, An - ger and in - gra - ti - tude, As we

death and res - ur - rec - tion o - ver sin the vict - 'ry
heav'n - ly throne of mer - cy, Where Christ's in - ter - ced - ing
loves each hum - ble sin - ner, Our re - pen - tant cry will
these con - fess be - fore You may our spir - its be re -

won;   Hear our hum - ble   sup - pli - ca - tion,   as we
now.   Bur-dened long   by   our trans-gres - sions, Peace and
heed.   Though the guilt   of   our trans-gres - sions does your
newed.   May we know the   full as - sur - ance   that to

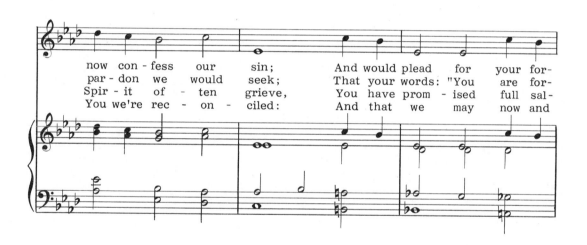

now con - fess our   sin;   And would plead   for   your for -
par - don we would   seek;   That your words: "You   are for -
Spir - it of - ten   grieve,   You have prom - ised   full sal -
You we're rec - on - ciled: And that we   may   now and

give - ness   and your bless - ed peace with - in.
giv - en," We may hear You soft - ly speak.
va - tion Un - to those who do be - lieve.
ev - er walk be - fore You un - de - filed.

Tune copyrighted by Skinner Chávez-Melo. Used by permission.

16 Great Men and Women of the Faith

Mary N. Hawkes, 1983

WELLINGTON SQUARE C.M.D.
Guy Warrack, 1900–?

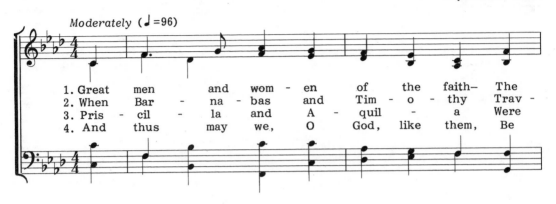

Moderately (♩=96)

1. Great men and wom - en of the faith— The
2. When Bar - na - bas and Tim - o - thy Trav -
3. Pris - cil - la and A - quil - a Were
4. And thus may we, O God, like them, Be

fol - lowers of the Way Dis - band - ed, sad, at
ersed a - long with Paul, On jour - neys far oe'r
friends of Paul's from Rome, Tent - mak - ers, fol-lowers
fol - lowers of the Way; We ask no price, no

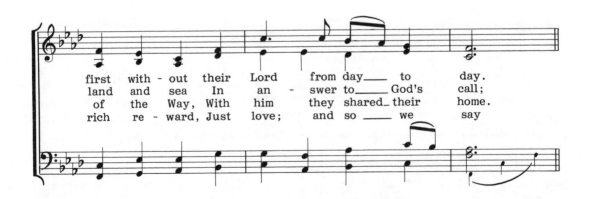

first with - out their Lord from day to day.
land and sea In an - swer to God's call;
of the Way, With him they shared their home.
rich re - ward, Just love; and so we say

Soon knew they had a task to do To
Kind Bar - na - bas the poor to save His
On riv - er bank near Phil - ip - pi Paul
That we will al - so fol - low Christ And

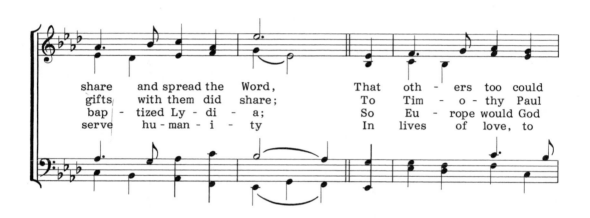

share and spread the Word, That oth - ers too could
gifts with them did share; To Tim - o - thy Paul
bap - tized Ly - di - a; So Eu - rope would God
serve hu - man - i - ty In lives of love, to

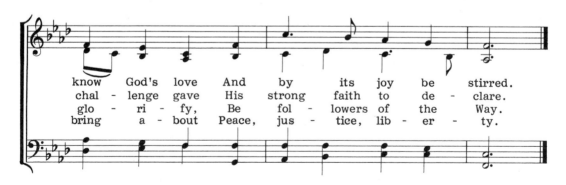

know God's love And by its joy be stirred.
chal - lenge gave His strong faith to de - clare.
glo - ri - fy, Be fol - lowers of the Way.
bring a - bout Peace, jus - tice, lib - er - ty.

17 Hail the Kingdom

J. Robert Zinn

15.15 with Refrain.
Laini Zinn

1. Hail the King-dom, like a ban-quet that a king gave for his son,
2. Peo-ple gath-ered by the thou-sands hun-gry for the Mas-ter's word.
3. Je-sus found a greed-y sin-ner up a tree in Jer-i-cho.
4. Eat-ing break-fast in the morn-ing by the Lake of Gal-i-lee,

First the cho-sen guests re-fused him, then he wel-comed ev-'ry-one.
Bod-ies fed with loaves and fish-es went to do the news they'd heard.
Af-ter sup-per, new Zac-cha-eus gave to help the King-dom grow.
Je-sus told a lov-ing Pe-ter, "Feed my sheep and fol-low me."

Refrain

Broth-ers, sis-ters, share the ban-quet of the boun-ty God out-poured

For the found-ing of the king-dom in the Christ, the liv-ing Lord.

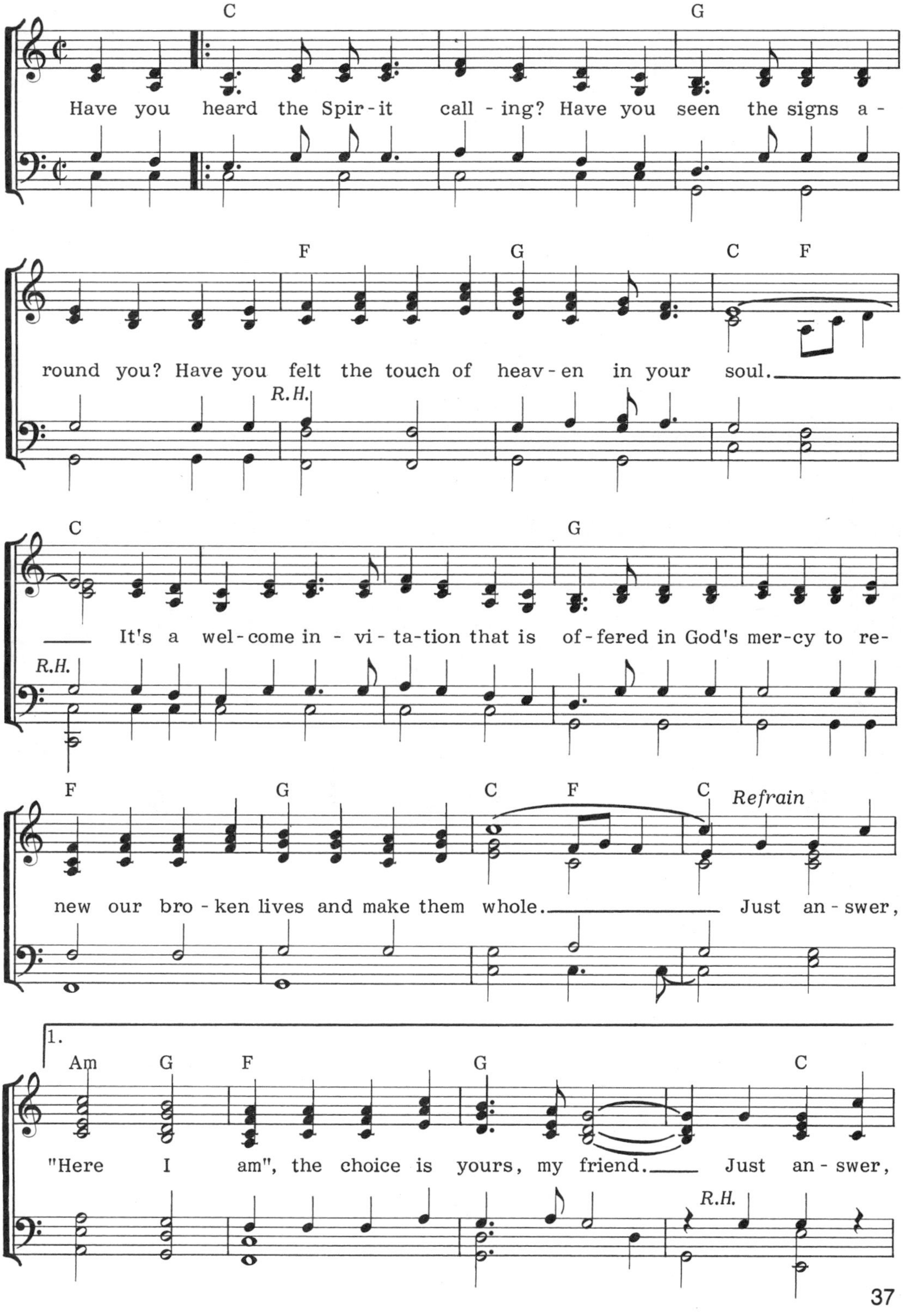

Have You Heard the Spirit Calling? 18

Ruth S. Sandberg

Irregular
Ruth S. Sandberg

C G
Have you heard the Spir - it call - ing? Have you seen the signs a -
F G C F
round you? Have you felt the touch of heav - en in your soul.
R.H.
C G
It's a wel - come in - vi - ta - tion that is of - fered in God's mer - cy to re -
R.H.
F G C F C
Refrain
new our bro - ken lives and make them whole. Just an - swer,
1.
Am G F G C
"Here I am", the choice is yours, my friend. Just an - swer,
R.H.

If You Want Food for Thought

(Think About Hunger)

Glenn Wallace

Irregular
Glenn Wallace

20 It's Hard to Have Hope

(Generation for Peace)

Don Eaton

Irregular with Refrain
Don Eaton

1. It's hard to have hope if you think you're a - lone in your
2. __ Par - ents of peace rais - ing child - ren of hope with the

strug - gle to make peace come true.___ But__ mil - lions of peo - ple___
cour - age to act on their dreams.___ For a pres - ent and fu - ture where

all 'round the earth have formed the peace cir - cle with you.___
peace be - comes real and each per - son lives what love means.___

21   Jesus Christ Frees and Unites

Gary L. Miller

CHRISTUS LIBERATOR
Irregular with Refrain
Gary L. Miller
Arr. Evelyn C. Miller

Refrain

Je - sus Christ frees and u - nites___ us all.

We are one to heed the call. Chil - dren we, tri -

um - phant - ly, glo - ry bring his name.

1. The Christ who makes us one, the Christ who makes us
2. To give as Christ would give, to care as Christ would
3. He suf - fered much for us, a - bove, be - yond us

free, the Christ who brings us lib - er - a - tion,
care, to heal all hu - man bro - ken - ness, to
all, He asks us now to love each oth - er

calls us all__ to__ be. To - day we must be -
share as Christ__ would__ share. The time to start is
as He first__ loved__ us. His pres - ence gives us

gin to live be - yond our - selves, to live a life of
now. Let's seek to - geth - er how u - nit - ed we can
hope in o - ver - com - ing strife, to bring the day of

D.C.

lib - er - ty in Je - sus to be free.
tru - ly be His bo - dy in the world.
love and joy He prom - ised with His life.

22

Journey Together With Me

(On Our Way)

Ruth S. Sandberg

ON OUR WAY, Irregular with Refrain
Ruth S. Sandberg

1. ___ Jour - ney to - geth - er with me_____ a -
2. ___ Dreams___ will car - ry us on_____
3. We sing,___ we dance and we pray,_____ Cre -
4. We dance through our joy and our pain,_____ We

cross___ the bridge to the fu - ture.
Joy - ful - ly in - to the sun - rise. We___
a - tor of all our to - mor - rows. For the
sing through our tears and our laugh - ter. A___

Jour-ney to - geth-er with me._____ A___ voice is call - ing in
hope in the prom-ise of dawn_____ And the voice that calls us in
glo - ry of ev - 'ry new day_____ And the voice that calls us in
rain-bow will fol - low the rain_____ And___ still the voice calls in

Descant

Al - le - lu - ia, Al - le - lu - ia, Al - le -

Love to
Love to
Love to   Look for the sky, fol - low the rain - bow,
Love to

lu - ia, Al - le - lu - ia. Al - le -

Reach for the stars and we're on our way.

Let Us Break Bread Together and Be Free 23

Wayne Bradley Robinson

LET US BREAK BREAD, 10.10 with Refrain
Afro-American Spiritual,
harm. David Hurd

1. Let us break bread to-geth-er and be free._____ Let us
2. Let us drink wine to-geth-er and be free._____ Let us

break bread to - geth-er and be free._____
drink wine to - geth-er and be free._____

Refrain

When I stand on my feet, with my face to the ris - ing sun, O____

Lord, have mer-cy on me.

3. Let us praise God to-geth-er and be free._____ Let us

praise God to - geth-er and be free._____

Many and Great, O God

Dakota Indian Hymn
arr. F. Philip Frazier

LACQUIPARLE Irregular
Sioux Indian Melody

1. Man-y and great, O God, are thy things, Mak-er of
2. Grant un-to us com-mun-ion with thee, Thou star-a-

earth and sky; Thy hands have set the heav-ens with stars;
bid-ing One; Come un-to us and dwell with___ us,

Thy fin-gers spread the moun-tains and plains. Lo, at thy
With thee are found the gifts of___ life. Bless us with

word the wa-ters were formed; Deep seas o-bey thy voice.
life that has no___ end, E-ter-nal life with thee.

The Dakota Indian Hymnal was compiled in 1879 by Rev. Thomas Williamson and Rev. Stephen Return Riggs, Presbyterian and Congregational missionaries to the Dakota Indians. The words to this song reflect an understanding of Jeremiah. F. Philip Frazier, who paraphrased the words, was a grandson of Artemas Ehnamani, the first ordained minister of the Dakota tribe. Frazier, too, was an ordained minister, and he and his wife were fine singers who gave concerts to raise money for their work among the Indians.

25 O Lord, Whose Everlasting Will is Given

(A Hymn for World Peace)

Waldo Beach

DONA PACEM 10.10.10.10.
Waldo Beach

1. O   Lord,   whose   ev   -   er   last - ing   will___ is   giv'n   That   hu - man - kind   should   learn   to   live   in   peace,
2. Grant   us   who   stand   be - hind   the   walls___ of   pride   Of   race   or   na - tion   and   im - per - ial   power
3. We   hold   in   store   the   wea - pons   of___our   death,   The   bombs   that   could   be   used   in   wan - ton   strife
4. Where   hu - man   skills   in   science   have   brought_us   close   As   neigh - bors   liv - ing   in   a   glo - bal   town,
5. Trans - late   our   prayer,   "Thy   will   be   done___ on   earth,"   To   deeds   that   build   new   struct - ures   of   ac - cord

Whose fear - less pro - phets,
The grace to know and
And make thy love - ly
Teach us to find our
A - mong all na - tions,

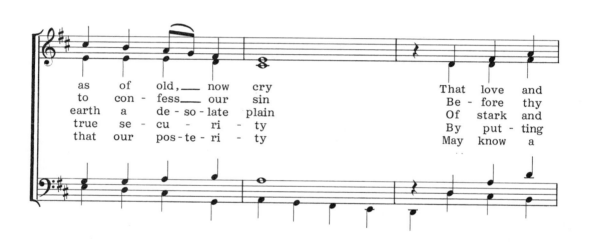

as of old, __ now cry
to con - fess __ our sin
earth a de - so - late plain
true se - cu - ri - ty
that our pos - te - ri - ty

That love and
Be - fore thy
Of stark and
By put - ting
May know a

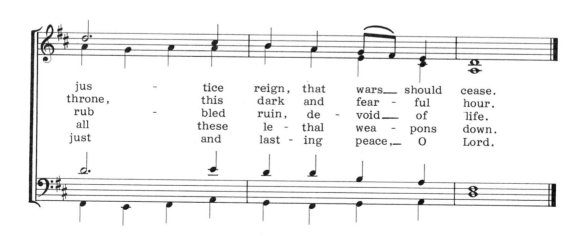

jus - tice reign, that wars __ should cease.
throne, this dark and fear - ful hour.
rub - bled ruin, de - void __ of life.
all these le - thal wea - pons down.
just and last - ing peace, __ O Lord.

26 Peace Be With You

(A Four–Part Round)

Anonymous

4.4.6.6.4.
Anonymous

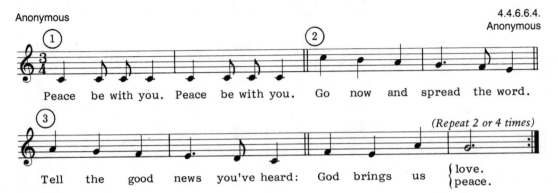

Peace be with you. Peace be with you. Go now and spread the word.

Tell the good news you've heard: God brings us { love. peace.

(Repeat 2 or 4 times)

Save the Earth and Save Her People

(Heart of God)

Susan Savell

HEART OF GOD 15.15.12.12.8.10.
Susan Savell

1. Save the earth and save her peo - ple from dis - as - ter
2. Gone are all the old il - lu - sions that the plan - et
3. All the child - ren of cre - a - tion watch our lives to
4. Lis - ten now your daugh - ters gath - er to dis - cov - er

and des - pair,_____ In our hearts there grows a sad - ness
can sur vive,_____ All the ways we waste her boun - ty
see if we_____ live the ho - ly truths we ut - ter,
and de - clare_____ in the pow - er of your Spir - it

and a fear too deep to bear_____ that the last days are dawn - ing, the
with - out car - ing to pro - vide_____ for_____ lands that are weep - ing as
if we've found a way to be_____ at_____ home like a moth - er and
is the call for us to dare_____ to_____ see with com - pas - sion to

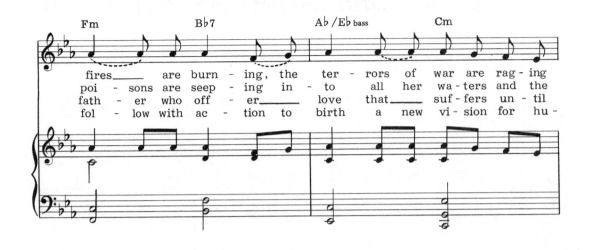

fires____ are burn - ing, the ter - rors of war are rag - ing
poi - sons are seep - ing in - to all her wa - ters and the
fath - er who off - er____ love that____ suf - fers un - til
fol - low with ac - tion to birth a new vi - sion for hu -

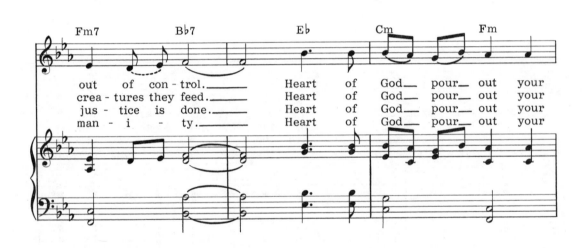

out of con - trol.____ Heart of God__ pour__ out your
crea - tures they feed.____ Heart of God__ pour__ out your
jus - tice is done.____ Heart of God__ pour__ out your
man - i - ty.____ Heart of God__ pour__ out your

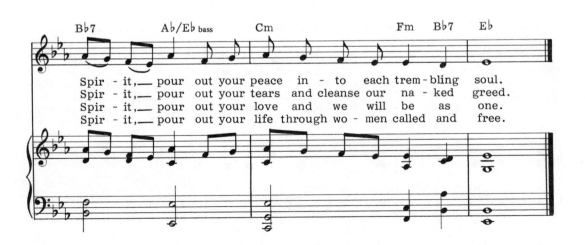

Spir - it,__ pour out your peace in - to each trem - bling soul.
Spir - it,__ pour out your tears and cleanse our na - ked greed.
Spir - it,__ pour out your love and we will be as one.
Spir - it,__ pour out your life through wo - men called and free.

Sobre Estas Tierras

Federico J. Pagura

REX 10.10.11.11 with Refrain
Skinner Chávez-Melo

1. So-bre es-tas tie-rras que el su-dor re-gó por tan-tos si-glos
2. Pue-blos can-sa-dos de tan-to ge-mir, ba-jo su a-lien-to
3. Más que o-tros mun-dos, quie-re él con-quis-tar la ciu-da-de la

de san-gre y do-lor, ve-mos le-van-tar-se ya de
han de re-vi-vir; nues-tros cuer-pos y al-mas vie-ne a
de la hu-ma-ni-dad; quie-re a to-dos dar-nos nue-vo

nue-vo el sol, por-que Dios pro-cla-ma su li-be-ra-ción.
res-tau-rar, pues él trae jus-ti-cia; él es nues-tra paz.
co-ra-zón, don-de el o-dio mue-ra y triun-fe el a-mor.

Estribillo *(Refrain)*

Cris - to quie - re ya rom - per ca - de - nas de o - pre - sión;

lle - ga a nues - tros pue - blos ple - na re - den - ción.

ple - na re - den - ción.

Somos Uno en Cristo

Anonymous

Irregular
Anonymous

So - mos u - no en Cris - to, so - mos u - no,___ u - no só - lo,___ só - lo u - no.___ So - mos u - no en Cris - to, so - mos u - no,___ u - no só - lo,___ só - lo u - no.___ Un so - lo Dios, un so - lo Se - ñor, u - na so - la fe, un so - lo a - mor, un so - lo bau - tis - mo, un so - lo Es - pí - ri - tu,___ y_e - se es nues - tro Con - so - la - dor.

30 Spirit Embracing Daughters

Dosia Carlson

MILWAUKEE 11.7.11.7.14.14.
Dosia Carlson

1. Spir - it em - brac - ing daugh-ters em - brac - ing sons, Pour out your Pow - er and peace;_____ Help us ac - cept with joy your prom - ise of
2. Spir - it in - vit - ing el - ders, in - vit - ing young, To dream of how we might live,_____ Send us a ho - ly vi - sion filled with Sha -
3. Spir - it en - fold - ing ra - ces, en - fold - ing tribes, Blend-er of cul - tures and creeds, _____ Guide us in ce - le - brat - ing dif - fer - ing

life, Grant that our riv - al - ries cease._____ We are
lom; Deep - en the care that we give._____ We are
gifts, Lead forth to ac - tion and deeds._____ We are

called,_____ we are free_____ to de - clare God's
called,_____ we are free_____ to af - firm what
called,_____ we are free_____ to res - pond with

won - der - ful grace:_____ We are called,_____ we are
God's love has done:_____ We are called,_____ we are
bo - dy and soul:_____ We are called,_____ we are

free_____ to pro - claim good news in this place._____
free_____ to bring jus - tice to ev - ery one._____
free_____ to be - come u - nit - ed and whole._____

31 The Doubts of My Faith

(Dayspring)

Larry Reimer

FOUNDATION 11.11.11.11.
Melody from *The Sacred Harp*,
1844, harm. Charles H. Heaton

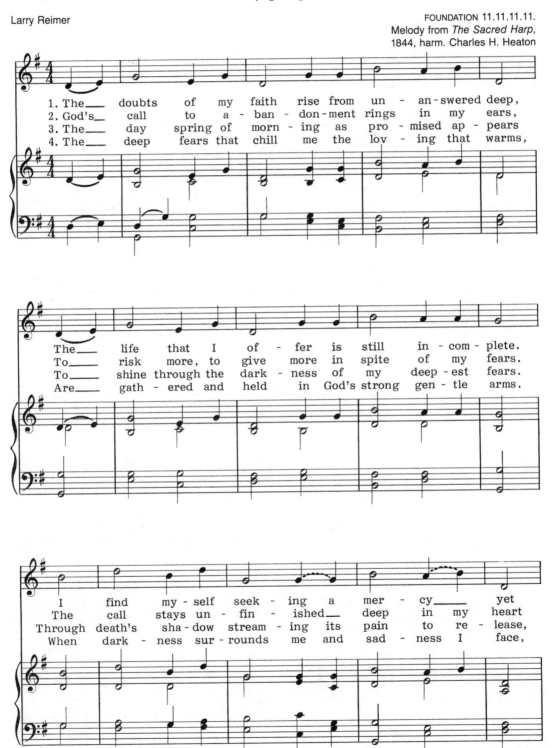

1. The doubts of my faith rise from un-an-swered deep,
2. God's call to a-ban-don-ment rings in my ears,
3. The day spring of morn-ing as pro-mised ap-pears
4. The deep fears that chill me the lov-ing that warms,

The life that I of-fer is still in-com-plete.
To risk more, to give more in spite of my fears.
To shine through the dark-ness of my deep-est fears.
Are gath-ered and held in God's strong gen-tle arms.

I find my-self seek-ing a mer-cy yet
The call stays un-fin-ished deep in my heart
Through death's sha-dow stream-ing its pain to re-lease,
When dark-ness sur-rounds me and sad-ness I face,

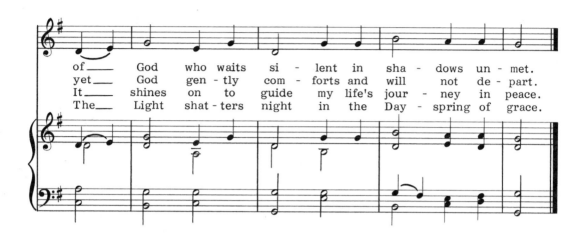

of___ God who waits si - lent in sha - dows un - met.
yet___ God gen - tly com - forts and will not de - part.
It___ shines on to guide my life's jour - ney in peace.
The___ Light shat - ters night in the Day - spring of grace.

Tune © 1967 Bethany Press. Used by permission.

32   This Do in Memory of Me

Wayne Bradley Robinson

ST. BOTOLPH C.M.
Gordon Slater,
1896–1979

1. This do in mem - o - ry____ of me; Eat
2. This do in mem - o - ry____ of me; Drink
3. We praise Your liv – ing mem - o - ry, Re -

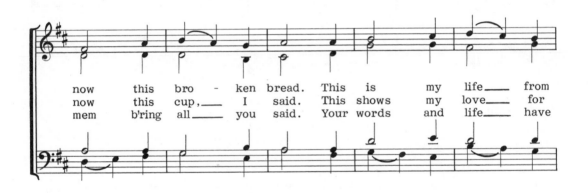

now this bro - ken bread. This is my life____ from
now this cup,____ I said. This shows my love____ for
mem b'ring all____ you said. Your words and life____ have

death__ set free,__ Here on my ta - ble spread.
all____ to see,__ Here on my ta - ble spread.
set____ us free,__ Here through your ta - ble spread.

This Is My Song

Lloyd Stone, 1912
Georgia Harkness, 1891,
Stanza 3

FINLANDIA 10.10.10.10.10.10.
Jean Sibelius

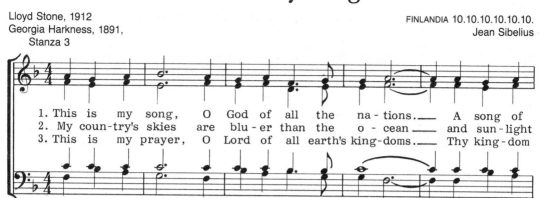

1. This is my song, O God of all the na-tions.___ A song of
2. My coun-try's skies are blu-er than the o-cean___ and sun-light
3. This is my prayer, O Lord of all earth's king-doms.___ Thy king-dom

peace for lands a-far and mine.___ This is my
beams on clo-ver-leaf and pine.___ But oth-er
come, on earth thy will be done.___ Let Christ be

home, the coun-try where my heart is;___ Here are my
lands have sun-light too and clo-ver,___ And skies are
lift-ed up till all will serve Him,___ And hearts u-

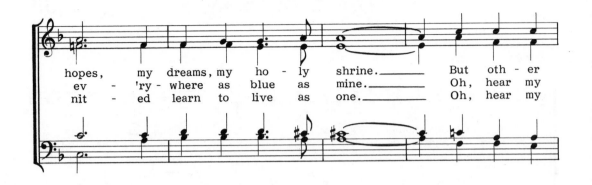

hopes, my dreams, my ho - ly shrine. But oth - er
ev - 'ry - where as blue as mine. Oh, hear my
nit - ed learn to live as one. Oh, hear my

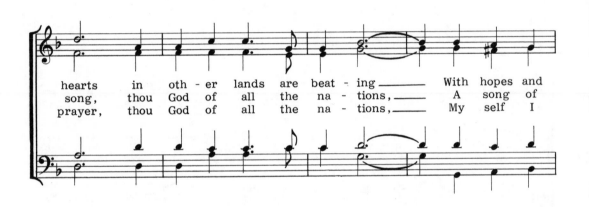

hearts in oth - er lands are beat - ing With hopes and
song, thou God of all the na - tions, A song of
prayer, thou God of all the na - tions, My self I

dreams as true and high as mine.
peace for their land and for mine.
give thee, let thy will be done.

Tune © Breitkopf & Härtel, Wiesbaden. Arrangement © 1933; by the Presbyterian Board of Christian Education; renewed 1961; from *The Hymnal*. Reproduced by permission of The Westminster Press, Philadelphia, PA. Words copyrighted by The Lorenz Corporation. Used by permission.

Though Wars are Fought

34

(Song of Unity)

Fran Vowel

ST. PETER C.M.
Alexander Robert Reinagle,
1799–1877

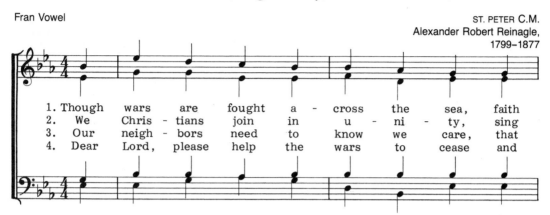

1. Though wars are fought a - cross the sea, faith
2. We Chris - tians join in u - ni - ty, sing
3. Our neigh - bors need to know we care, that
4. Dear Lord, please help the wars to cease and

spreads through-out the land, For God's will doth reign
praise to God a - bove, We trust in God so
we cry shame - less tears, For them we lift our
ease the trou - bled souls, Let them be free to

end - less - ly, God know - eth what's at hand.
faith - ful - ly, We share God's peace and love.
hearts in prayer, for God to calm their fears.
live in peace, Make u - ni - ty their goal.

35 Ukutemwa Kwaba Yesu

(The Love of Jesus Relieve My Heart)

Anonymous Zambian
Tr. David Edward Pattee
and Kurt R. Hansen

KASEMBE 9.9.16.
Zambian Bemba Traditional
arr. David Edward Pattee
and Kurt R. Hansen

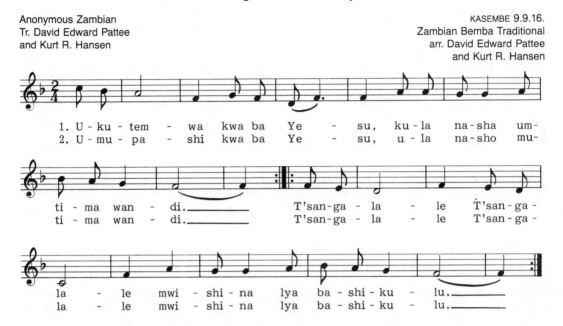

1. U - ku - tem - wa kwa ba Ye - su, ku - la na - sha um-
2. U - mu - pa - shi kwa ba Ye - su, u - la na - sho mu-

ti - ma wan - di._____ T'san - ga - la - le T'san - ga -
ti - ma wan - di._____ T'san - ga - la - le T'san - ga -

la - le mwi - shi - na lya ba - shi - ku - lu._____
la - le mwi - shi - na lya ba - shi - ku - lu._____

English Translation:
The love of Jesus relieve my heart.
The spirit of Jesus relieve my heart.
Let us rejoice in the name of the Lord.

We All Are One in Jesus Christ

Mary N. Hawkes, 1984

McKEE C.M.
Black Melody
Adapted by Harry T. Burleigh, 1866–1949

These words are written in honor of Martin Luther King, Jr. Harry T. Burleigh (1866–1949), the grandson of a slave, arranger of this melody, wrote,

The plantation songs known as "spirituals" are the spontaneous outbursts of intense religious fervor, and had their origin chiefly in camp meetings, revivals and other religious exercises. They were never 'composed,' but sprang into life, ready made, from the white heat of religious fervor . . . as the simple, ecstatic utterance of wholly untutored minds. (From *Guide to the Pilgrim Hymnal*.)

37   We Come Rejoicing O'er the Paths

This Far by Faith

Paul R. Gregory

YORKSHIRE 10.10.10.10.10.10.
John Wainright (c. 1723–1768)

1. We come re-joic-ing o'er the paths we've trod And in the
2. The way is marked with names of those whose lives Spelled out in
3. Where once the vast-ness of a world un-known Put faith and
4. The chal-lenge now: those mar-gins where the world As-signs its

her-i-tage of faith we share: Vi-sion and strength— both
ser-vice what their words pro-claimed; And in our day the
un-tried cour-age to the test, To-day the depths of
pris'-ners, poor and hun-gry ones. The call: to see true

gifts from You, O God, No jour-ney e'er be-yond your
church they nur-tured strives, Seek-ing ful-fill-ment still to
hu-man hearts, we own, Pre-sent the chal-lenge that de-
free-dom's flag un-furled, And love o'er-throw op-pres-sion's

lov-ing care. With joy we cel-e-brate a jour-ney
be at-tained. Thus far has faith brought us a-long the
mands our best. By faith we reached those far hor-i-zons
cru-el thrones. This far by faith we've come our pil-grim

done And turn in faith to jour-neys just be-gun.
way And taught us hope for mis-sion's break-ing day.
past, Press on in faith God's love will hold us fast.
way; God's guid-ing hand e-nough for each new day!

We Hail a Day

Paul R. Gregory

KINGSFOLD C.M.D.
English melody; adapt. and harmony,
Ralph Vaughan Williams (1872–1958)

1. We___ hail a day when storm - driv'n youth took___
2. Un - like - ly launch - ing pad for truth That___
3. God's___ might - y pow - er still com - mands A___

re - fuge from___ the blast, Turned___ bear - ers of com -
shelt - 'ring pile___ of hay Too___ un - de - signed, too
mis - sion to___ our world; God's___ lib - er - at - ing

mand - ing truth A___ chal - lenge that___ would last, We___
mean, un - couth to___ be the Lord___ God's way. Yet___
word de - mands Love's ban - ner be___ un - furled. Oh___

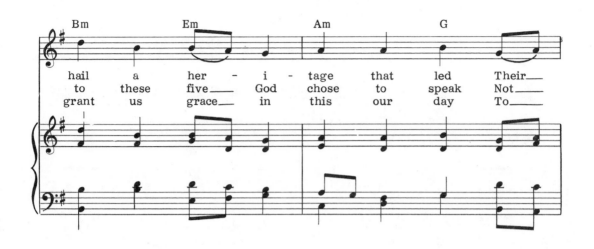

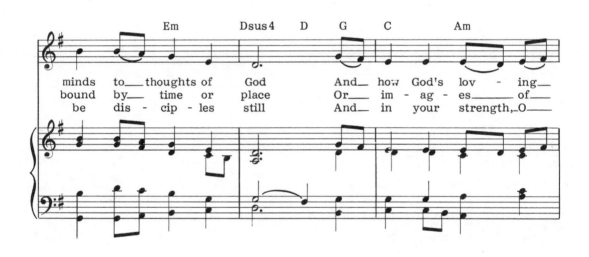

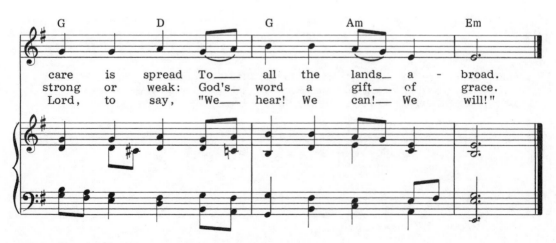

We Have Come to this Moment

(Song of Peace)

39

Barbara VanHorn

DUTCHER-WALLS Irregular
Barbara VanHorn

1. We have come to this mo - ment, __ with
2. As __ friends we have gath - ered __ to
3. We have come to this mo - ment, __ with

hearts __ o - pened __ wide Say-ing "Yes!" to the
hold the world __ in our love, For we know that this
goes be - yond all space and time, To __ share with each

fu - ture, __ that peace __ can __ a - bide. And the
un - ion __ brings free - dom like __ the __ dove. For in
oth - er, __ the joy of learn-ing to be kind. And the

bless - ings __ of the Spir - it __ rest up - on this, our
join - ing __ to - geth - er __ all the hope of our
bless - ing __ of the Spir - it __ rests up - on all our

choice, To share love with each oth - er __ and __
lives, We are al - so Peace mak - ers __ for a
hearts, Stand be - fore God's __ pres - ence, __ this __

1.
sing of peace as in one voice.

2. and 3.
wea - ry world in search of ties.
jour - ney now a - bout to start.

40   We Stand at the Future's Threshold

Paul R. Gregory

IN BABILONE 87.87.D
Melody from *Oude en Nieuwe Hollantse Boerenlities en Contradansen*, 1710;
Harmony by Charles Winfred Douglas (1867–1944)

1. We stand at the future's thresh - old,
2. Midst the teem - ing cit - ies mil - lions,
3. O - pen heart - ed in ex - chang - es
4. Build - ing jus - tice as the bul - wark
5. Son of God, e - ter - nal Sav - ior,

Grate - ful for God's guid - ing hand, Ask - ing no pro -
Wit - ness to God's bound - less love, Reach - ing for each
With the faith - ful not our own, Trust - ing God's way
Of the peace that God would give, Mak - ing sac - ri -
Source of life and truth and grace, We would ask no

tec - ted strong-hold, Called to be a pil - grim band,
sys - tem's lost - ones, Seek - ing jus - tice with each move;
with these strang - ers Not to leave the truth un - known,
fice the hall - mark Of the life we're called to live:
spe - cial fa - vor, With the low - liest seek our place,

Seek - ing ___ ev - er for new vi - sion
Grant us ___ cour - age, strength and pa - tience
Join - ing ___ them in shared en - dea - vor
Grant us, ___ God, to bear this wit - ness
Know the ___ in - as - much of serv - ing,

Or the ___ Gos - pel for our ___ day, ___ Mov - ing ___ for - ward
To con - tend with vi - cious ___ pow'r ___ Lead us ___ for - ward
Where we ___ have Christ's clear com - mand, ___ We've a ___ faith that
To the ___ Prince of Peace and ___ move ___ For - ward ___ with our
Have your ___ Cross as our com - mand: ___ Lead us ___ in this

in God's ___ mis - sion With our ___ faith to ___ show ___ the ___ way.
in the ___ Faith whence We find ___ hope in ___ test - ing's ___ hour.
calls us ___ ev - er Tow'rd this ___ good earth's ___ prom - ised ___ land.
Faith's own ___ ac - cess To the ___ life of ___ hope ___ and ___ peace.
Faith un - swerv - ing For - ward ___ as Your ___ pil - grim ___ band.

71

41   "You Came to Quench My Thirst"

Whenever You Do It

Laini Zinn

Irregular
Laini Zinn

Alleluia, Christ is Risen

(Easter Anthem–SATB)

Celia Wight

Celia Wight

Al-le-lu, Al - le-lu-ia, Christ is ris'n, Al - le-lu-ia. From the dead, Al - le-lu-ia.

2nd time
to Coda ⊕ *rit.*

As He said, Al - le-lu-ia. Praise Him the ris - en Lord. Al - le - lu-ia.

Slower

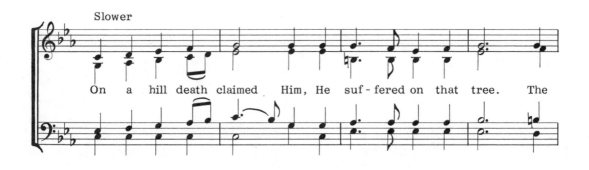

On a hill death claimed Him, He suf-fered on that tree. The

tomb was sealed, But soon re-vealed the Lord in vic-to-ry.___

Glor-ious now be - hold Him, in tri - umph shall He reign. All

glo - ry, laud and hon - or, to Him who lives a - gain. Al - le -

lu, Al - le - lu, Al - le - lu, Al - le - lu.

le - lu - ia, Al - le - lu - ia!
le - lu, Al - le - lu - ia, Al - le - lu - ia!

43 Christmas Trilogy

I. Christmas Lullaby

Laini Zinn

Laini Zinn

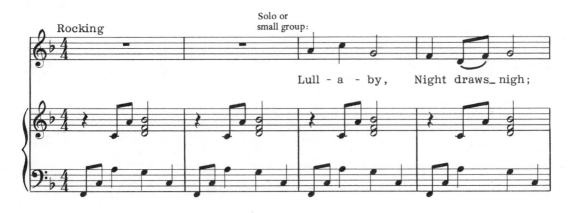

Lull - a - by, Night draws_ nigh;

Go to sleep my_ son. Sing for joy, this lit - tle boy

An - gels chant the won-drous sto - ry:

is God's Ho - ly One. Oooo - oooo oooo - oooo

44   Christmas Trilogy

II. Sing Noel

Laini Zinn

Laini Zinn

daily duty. See the Christ Child, born in beauty."
joyful measure. Bowed before God's new-born treasure.

3. God gives the gift of life and love to ev'ry one. God shows pure love by
4. "Glo - ri - a in ex - cel - sis De - o." Glo - ri - a

Divisi No - el, No - el,

sending us an only Son. Sing No - el, No - el, No - el, oh
in ex - cel - sis De - o.

No - el, No - el. No - el! No - el!

sing No - el, No - el, No - el. el. No - el! No - el!

45

Christmas Trilogy

III. As We Journey Toward Bethlehem

Laini Zinn   Laini Zinn

1. Cam-el bells re-call how the
2. See the guid-ing star o-ver

an-cient_ star_____ called_ forth three kings on a
all our_ lands_____ pierc-ing all our dark - est

quest._____ So they jour - neyed toward Beth - le -
skies,_____ as we jour - neyed toward Beth - le -

hem._____ There they brought rare gifts to the
hem._____ What a - waits us? What does our

man - ger_ stall,_____ Where the king of all lay in
God de - mand?_____ Will it lead us to a sur -

rest._____ } God a - waits us; let us a - dore._____
prise?_____ }

He comes to shed pure light in a world so filled with fright.

Love and hope will lead us home to the Babe in Beth - le - hem.

So we trav - el to - ward the

love of the Lord of our life,_____ As we jour - ney

(A few higher voices)
Al -

le - lu - ia!_____

toward Beth - le - hem._____

Imagine If

46

Laini Zinn

Laini Zinn

Tarantelle style

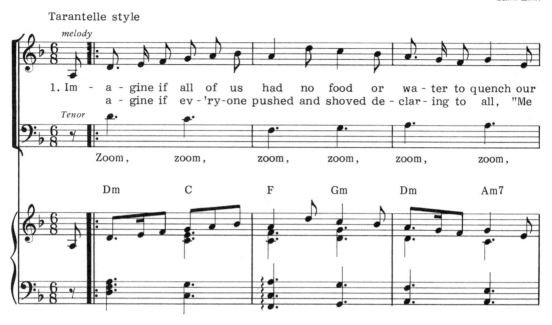

1. Im - a - gine if all of us had no food or wa - ter to quench our

a - gine if ev - 'ry-one pushed and shoved de - clar - ing to all, "Me

Zoom, zoom, zoom, zoom, zoom, zoom,

Dm   C   F   Gm   Dm   Am7

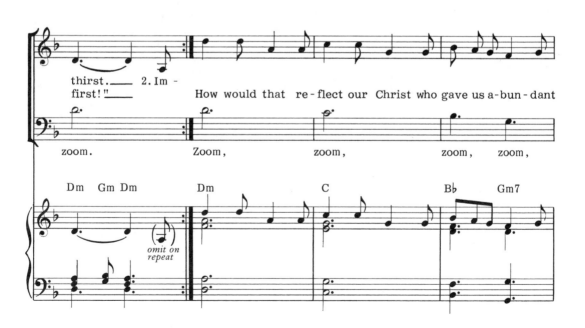

thirst.____ 2. Im -

first!"____

How would that re - flect our Christ who gave us a - bun - dant

zoom.   Zoom, zoom, zoom, zoom,

Dm Gm Dm   Dm   C   B♭ Gm7

omit on repeat

life?___ Im - a - gine a world in which no one cares; a world which is filled with

zoom. Zoom, zoom, zoom, zoom, zoom, zoom,

strife.___ There's plen - ty to eat if we on - ly would share, There's

zoom, zoom.

plen - ty of wa - ter to drink.___ God gives us our hearts filled with

lov - ing care, and gives us our minds to think.____ Im-

Fmaj7   C7   F   Gm   Asus   A

a tempo   Unison

a - gine if all of the world could learn to live for the com - mon good.____ Im-

Tenor
Zoom,   zoom,   zoom,   zoom,   zoom,   zoom,   zoom.

Dm   C   F   Gm   Dm   G/A   Dm Gm Dm

a - gine if all of the world could Love in sis - ter and broth - er - hood!____

Dm   C   F   Gm   Dm   G   A7   D

47

Let Us Call Upon God

(Introit)

Laini Zinn

Laini Zinn

Let us call up-on God who is our pow-er. Let us call up-on all that gives life and breath. Hal-le-lu-jah! to our Re-deem-er, our Cre-a-tor!

Oh Yah-weh! Oh Yah-weh! Hal-le-lu-jah! to our Re-deem-er, our Cre-a-tor!

Our Prayers Rise unto Thee

48

(A Lenten Introit)

Celia Wight

6.6.14.
Celia Wight

Our prayers rise un - to Thee. O Lamb of Cal - va -

ry. Pre - pare our hearts to bear Thy pain and

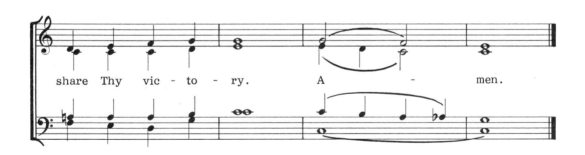

share Thy vic - to - ry. A - men.

49 Praise Ye the Lord

Psalm 150

Mary Kae Waytenick

Well-accented

(Organ) f

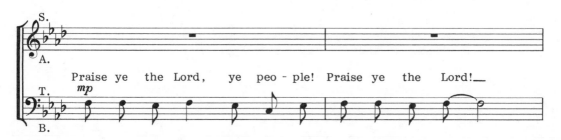

Praise ye the Lord, ye peo - ple! Praise ye the Lord!_

mp

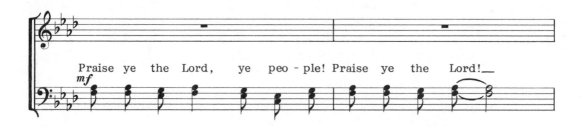

Praise ye the Lord, ye peo - ple! Praise ye the Lord!_

mf

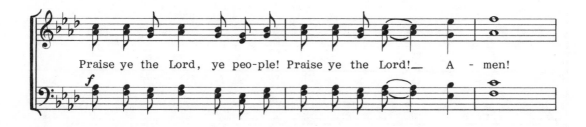

Praise ye the Lord, ye peo-ple! Praise ye the Lord!_ A - men!

f

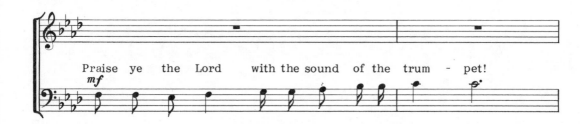

Praise ye the Lord with the sound of the trum - pet!

mf

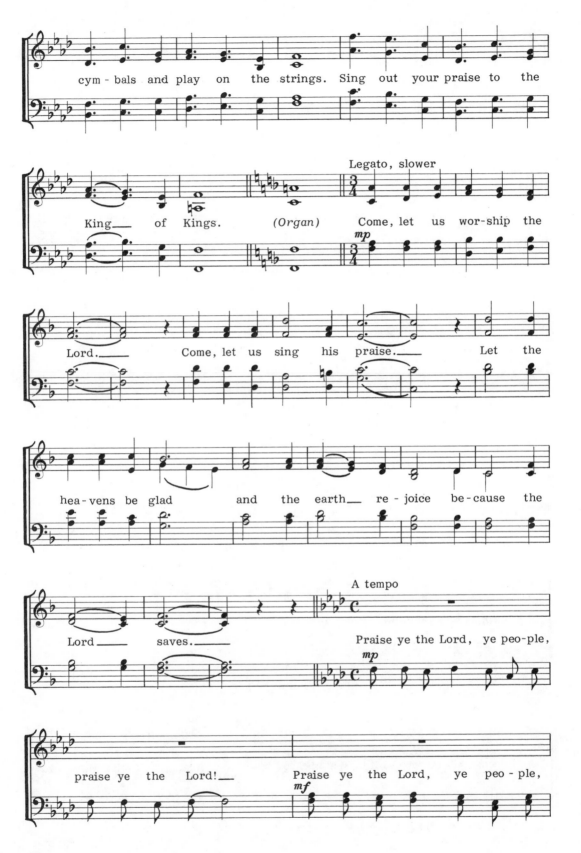

cym - bals and play on the strings. Sing out your praise to the

Legato, slower

King___ of Kings. (Organ) Come, let us wor-ship the

Lord.___ Come, let us sing his praise.___ Let the

hea-vens be glad and the earth__ re - joice be-cause the

A tempo

Lord ___ saves.___ Praise ye the Lord, ye peo-ple,

praise ye the Lord!__ Praise ye the Lord, ye peo-ple,

praise ye the Lord!_ Praise ye the Lord, ye peo - ple,

Praise ye the Lord!_ A - men! Praise ye the Lord with the sound of the

trum - pet! Praise ye the Lord with the sound of the

Praise ye the Lord with the sound of the trum - pet!

lute! Sing to the Lord a song so

Praise ye the Lord with the sound of the lute!

an - y who sing a - long will join in the throng of those who

Sing to the Lord a song so an - y who sing a - long will

praise Him!_ A - men.

join in the throng of those who praise Him._

50 This is the Lord's House

(Introit)

Dixie L. Wheeler

5.6.5.5.12.5.6.
Dixie L. Wheeler

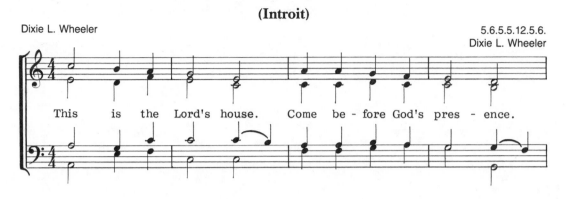

This is the Lord's house. Come be-fore God's pres - ence.

This is the Lord's house. Sing and praise and pray.

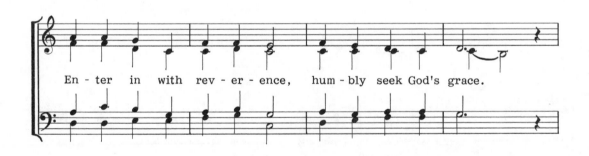

En - ter in with rev - er - ence, hum - bly seek God's grace.

This is the Lord's house. Let us come be - fore God.

We Come to Hear

(Introit)

Celia Wight

8.8.8.
Celia Wight

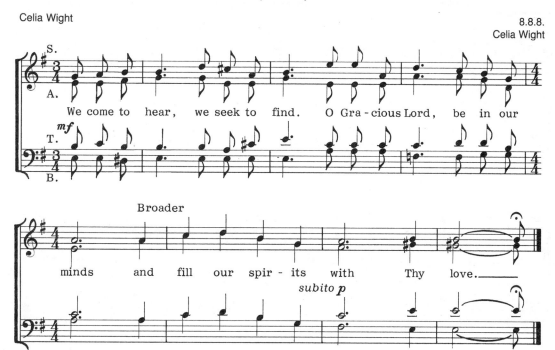

We come to hear, we seek to find. O Gra-cious Lord, be in our

Broader

minds and fill our spir - its with Thy love.

subito p

52   We Go Into the World

(Benediction Response)

Celia Wight

10.14.
Celia Wight

We go in-to Thy world with faith a-new. O grant us wis-dom, hope and love; Thy ho-ly work to do.

Index of Authors, Translators, and Sources

Raquel Achón, 7 (trans.)
Afro-American Spiritual, 11
Anonymous, 26, 29
Anonymous Zambian, 35
Waldo Beach, 25
Dosia Carlson, 30
James W. Crawford, 6, 10
Dakota Indian Hymn, 24
Don Eaton, 20
F. Philip Frazier, 24 (arr.)
Paul R. Gregory, 11 (adapt.), 37, 38, 40
Kurt R. Hansen, 35 (trans.)
Georgia Harkness, 33 (stanza 3)

Edwin Hatch, 3
Mary N. Hawkes, 1, 14, 16, 36
Jane Parker Huber, 4
Isaiah 61, 5
Richard B. Kozelka, 12
Luke 4:18, 5
Gary L. Miller, 21
Federico J. Pagura, 28
David Edward Pattee, 35 (trans.)
Psalm 150, 49
Larry Reimer, 31
Wayne Bradley Robinson, 23, 32
May Rowland, 9

Ruth S. Sandberg, 18, 22
Susan Savell, 27
Lillian Schwerdfager, 15
Lloyd Stone, 33
Barbara VanHorn, 39
Fran Vowel, 34
Glenn Wallace, 2, 19
Dixie L. Wheeler, 50
Celia Wight, 42, 48, 51, 52
Harriet Ilse.Ziegenhals, 8
J. Robert Zinn, 17
Laini Zinn, 3 (adapt.), 5 (adapt.), 7, 13, 41, 43, 44, 45, 46, 47

Index of Composers, Arrangers, and Sources

Afro-American Spiritual, 11, 23
Anonymous, 26, 29
Waldo Beach, 25
Black Melody, 36
Harry T. Burleigh, 36 (adapt.)
Dosia Carlson, 30
Skinner Chávez-Melo, 15, 28
David Cicchese, 12
Charles Winfred Douglas, 40 (harm.)
Don Eaton, 20
English Melody, 38
Genevan Psalter, 1551, 8 (abridged)
Kurt R. Hansen, 35 (arr.)
Charles H. Heaton, 31 (harm.)
David Hurd, 23 (harm.)

Evelyn C. Miller, 21 (arr.)
Gary L. Miller, 21
Melody from *Oude en Nieuwe Hollantse Boerenlities en Contradansen, 1710*, 40
Charles Hubert Hastings Parry, 4
David Edward Pattee, 35 (arr.)
Poitiers Antiphoner, 1746, 14
Henry Purcell, 6
Alexander Robert Reinagle, 34
Lily Rundle, 9
The Sacred Harp, 1844, 31
Ruth S. Sandberg, 18, 22
Susan Savell, 27
Martin G. Schneider, 1
Jean Sibelius, 33

Gordon Slater, 32
Sioux Indian Melody, 24
Thomas Tallis, 10
Barbara VanHorn, 39
Ralph Vaughan-Williams, 38 (adapt. and harm.)
John Wainwright, 37
Glenn Wallace, 2, 19
Guy Warrack, 16
Mary Kae Waytenick, 49
Dixie L. Wheeler, 50
Celia Wight, 42, 48, 51, 52
Zambian Bemba Traditional, 35
Laini Zinn, 3, 5, 7, 13, 17, 41, 43, 44, 45, 46, 47

Index of Tunes

Christus Liberator, 21
Dona Pacem, 25
Dutcher-Walls, 39
Finlandia, 33
Foundation, 31
Go Tell It On the Mountain, 11
Heart of God, 27
In Babilone, 40
Iste Confessor (Rouen), 14

Kasembe, 35
Kingsfold, 38
Lacquiparle, 24
Let Us Break Bread, 23
McKee, 36
Milwaukee, 30
On Our Way, 22
Pax, 9
Purdue, 7
Raquel, 15

Rex, 28
Rustington, 4
St. Botolph, 32
St. Peter, 34
The Eighth Tune, 10
Toulon, 8
Wellington Square, 16
Westminster Abbey, 6
Yorkshire, 37

References are to hymn-numbers, not page-numbers

Index of First Lines and Titles

References are to hymn-numbers, not page-numbers